Your Financial Revolution

THE POWER OF REST

GARY KEESEE

ISBN: 978-1-945930-09-6

Published by Free Indeed Publishers.
Distributed by Faith Life Now.

Faith Life Now
P.O. Box 779
New Albany, OH 43054
1-(888)-391-LIFE

You can reach Faith Life Now Ministries on the Internet at www.faithlifenow.com.

RW1B18
12.23

CONTENTS

QUESTIONS:
Fill in the blanks from your reading.

SCRIPTURES:
Dive into the Word of God.

THOUGHTS:
Respond to these prompts to go deeper.

KNOW THIS:
Meditate on these important standout statements.

PRAYER

INTRODUCTION

Rest. We all crave it.

Because we're tired. Tired of running the rat race. Tired of working harder and longer but never seeming to get any further. Tired of feeling stuck. Tired of worrying. Tired of not being happy.

But you don't have to live that way.

God didn't create you to be on the world's treadmill. He created you to live in His rest—a rest like no other—His Sabbath Rest. It's a place where your needs are met; where you're free from the rat race; free to find and prosper in your purpose and passion; where you're prospering past survival; and where you're demonstrating results to the world that are different than what they normally see.

You may find it hard to believe at this point, but I promise you what Drenda and I discovered about Kingdom living—about living a *life of rest*—is just as much available to you as it was, and is, to us.

My prayer is that, through this study, you'll discover the power of rest for yourself.

> *Come to me, all you who are weary and burdened, and I will give you rest. Take my yoke upon you and learn from me, for I am gentle and humble in heart, and you will find rest for your souls. For my yoke is easy and my burden is light.*
>
> —Matthew 11:28-30

CHAPTER 1

REST - THE BASICS

REST [rest] – to be placed or supported so as to stay in a specified position; an instance or period of relaxing or ceasing to engage in strenuous or stressful activity; relief or freedom, especially from anything that wearies, troubles, or disturbs.

Get off the Hamster Wheel

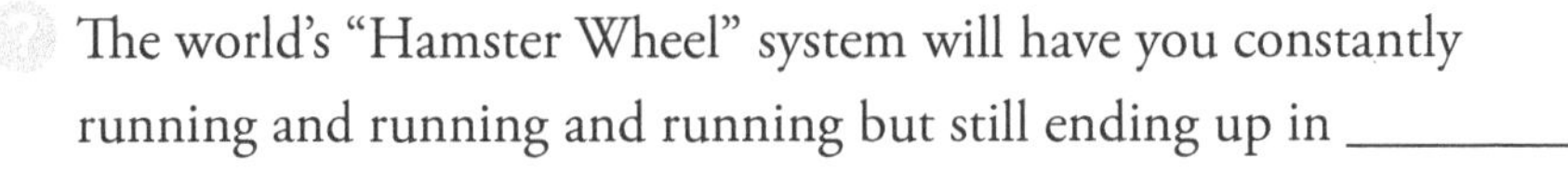

The world's "Hamster Wheel" system will have you constantly running and running and running but still ending up in ________ ____.

God's Kingdom System	The World's System
• Excitement to get to work on strategies and ideas from God	• Dread Mondays. Only look forward to weekends, vacations, or retirement.
• Energized by seeing the Kingdom of God operate	• Exhaustion
• Peace	• Drama, panic, and fear over when the next thing might go wrong
• Hope	• Little to no hope for a better future
• Life	• Survival

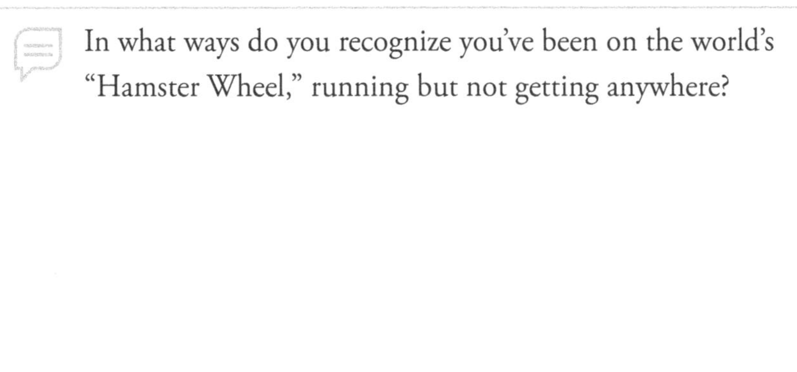

In what ways do you recognize you've been on the world's "Hamster Wheel," running but not getting anywhere?

You must learn God's Kingdom system of handling finances if you want to be free.

Flip the Switch

The Kingdom of God is a ______________________________, with ______________________________ that do not change.

KNOW THIS: YOU CAN LEARN THE LAWS OF THE KINGDOM OF GOD AND TAP INTO GOD'S POWER AND WISDOM TO CREATE THE WEALTH YOU NEED.

One ________________ from God can completely change your life.

You'll have to walk it out, but God will show you where to walk.

When you are living in God's rest, you can stay on ______________ and keep focused on your ______________.

What has God shown you about your assignment and/or purpose?

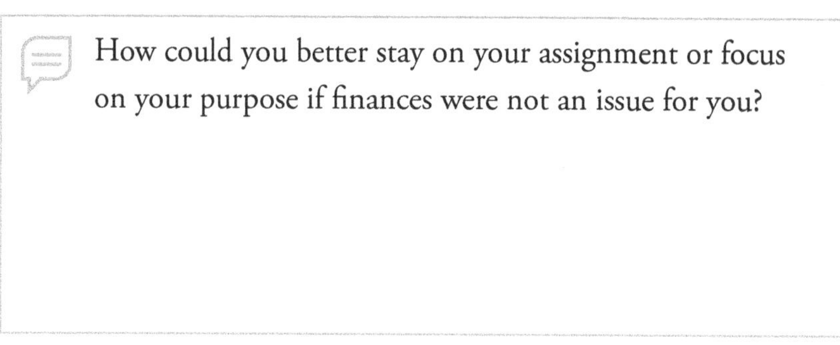
How could you better stay on your assignment or focus on your purpose if finances were not an issue for you?

When you're no longer living a life of survival, you can be about ______________________________.

Write out Matthew 6:25-32:

KNOW THIS: FINANCIAL STRESS WAS NEVER GOD'S PLAN—IN THE BEGINNING, OR FOR YOU TODAY.

Resting Place

No matter how much pressure you're under right now or what financial issues you're facing, God is bigger, and He can give you real rest.

Take some time this week to unplug—get off the world's "Hamster Wheel"—and get plugged in with Him.

"

Lord, thank You for showing me that Your Kingdom is a government with laws that do not change.

I repent for not taking the time to learn how Your Kingdom operates in regard to finances and for every financial mess I've ever gotten myself into.

I ask that you flip the switch and shine Your light on everything I'm reading in The Power of Rest *and in Your Word, so I can learn how Your Kingdom operates, see things I've never seen before, and live life differently than I've been living.*

In Jesus's name I pray, amen.

"

CHAPTER 2
LEGAL RIGHTS

REST [rest] – to be placed or supported so as to stay in a specified position; an instance or period of relaxing or ceasing to engage in strenuous or stressful activity; relief or freedom, especially from anything that wearies, troubles, or disturbs.

God desires to give you the answers to your financial chaos, but there are some things you must know regarding how the Kingdom operates before you will be able to tap into that kind of help.

Understanding the Kingdom and Your Place in It

In the literal sense, kingdom means the king's ________________.

A king's kingdom operates by the ________________ of the king.

His words become the ________________ that govern his domain and the lives of his citizens

A kingdom:

1. Functions under a king
2. Uses the word of the king to create the laws that govern his domain and the lives of his citizens.
3. Is a government with laws that enforce the king's laws on behalf of and on every legal citizen of that kingdom.

Ephesians 2:19 says you are not only a citizen of the Kingdom of God but also a member of His very own ________________, a son or daughter of the King.

Summarize Galatians 4:1-7 in your own words:

As a son or daughter of God, you already have the entire estate. You are a coheir with Jesus of all that God has.

What have you been begging God for that you didn't realize was already rightfully yours as a coheir with Jesus?

You don't have to ____________________ like a citizen of a country in order to be one.

It is a ________________________ matter that is satisfied by the fact that you were born there.

KNOW THIS: WHEN YOU'RE IN RIGHT STANDING WITH GOD AND YOUR LIFE IS BASED ON LAW INSTEAD OF HOW YOU FEEL, THINGS CHANGE!

Write out 1 John 5:14-15:

If you ask according to the laws of the King, you should already know that He will enforce His own law. Thus, you can be ____________________ in the outcome; there will be no guessing.

God's Kingdom is governed by ____________________, which are available to every citizen without partiality.

Read Mark 6:4-6 again. These Scriptures give us insight into how the Kingdom functions. Here, we see Jesus could not do any miracles in His hometown. Why?

The Importance of Faith

Your understanding of this most basic law of the Kingdom is life or death.

God is love, and the Word says love never fails.

What does fail, however, is God's ______________________________, His ability to intervene in the earth realm, which is produced by our ______________________.

Since man has jurisdiction in the earth realm, God cannot just do what He wants.

Your agreement with heaven, *your faith*, is needed, to give heaven jurisdiction to bring the power of God into that situation and produce righteousness.

Faith is ____
____.

Satan had to get Adam and Eve to believe, or align, themselves with him instead of with God.

In what ways do you recognize that you may have aligned your faith with the wrong kingdom in the past?

KNOW THIS: YOU CAN BE IN FAITH FOR WHAT GOD SAYS, OR YOU CAN BE IN FAITH FOR WHAT THE KINGDOM OF DARKNESS SAYS.

After Adam, who had the authority over the earth, cut off God's legal jurisdiction in the earth realm, God told him that his survival would be up to him, with hard labor and painful toil. I call this the ______________ ______________ system of survival.

God has to find a man or a woman in the earth realm who will come into ___________________________with Him, which opens the spiritual door for the Kingdom of God to have legal jurisdiction here.

____________________ must be present for the Kingdom of God to have jurisdiction here.

Romans 10:10 shows us the process.

Step 1: Your heart must believe or come into AGREEMENT with heaven.

Step 2: Your heart being in agreement makes it LEGAL for heaven to invade Earth and gives you the LEGAL right to have what heaven says.

Step 3: When you CONFESS your faith, you RELEASE it into the earth realm.

KNOW THIS: HEAVEN CANNOT MOVE UNLESS A MAN OR WOMAN WHO IS IN FAITH—OR AGREEMENT WITH HEAVEN—RELEASES THAT AUTHORITY INTO THE EARTH REALM! HEAVEN IS WAITING ON YOU!

Resting Place

Matthew 18:18 says that whatever you bind on earth will be bound in heaven and whatever you loose on earth will be loosed in heaven. Heaven can't be released into the earth realm without YOU.

Take some time this week to ask God to show you what you've been confessing and releasing into the earth realm and what you've been binding and loosing. Write down everything He tells you, and take action to replace those confessions with His promises.

> *Lord, thank You for showing me how Your Kingdom operates and for sending Jesus, so that I can be a citizen of your Kingdom and a coheir with Him of Your family business with Him!*
>
> *Help me to clear my mind and throw out any religious answers I've heard throughout my life that do not accurately portray Your character or that hinder me in any way from further understanding Your Kingdom and the rest You've already provided.*
>
> *Help me to be Your gatekeeper here on earth, with my heart and mind fully persuaded of what heaven says, releasing heaven's authority and power here in the earth realm.*
>
> *In Jesus's name I pray, amen.*

CHAPTER 3

THE KINGDOM IS YOUR ANSWER

REST [rest] – to be placed or supported so as to stay in a specified position; an instance or period of relaxing or ceasing to engage in strenuous or stressful activity; relief or freedom, especially from anything that wearies, troubles, or disturbs.

You Were Created to Live in the Seventh Day

> *Thus the heavens and the earth were completed in all their vast array. By the seventh day God had finished the work he had been doing; so on the seventh day he rested from all his work. And God blessed the seventh day and made it holy, because on it he rested from all the work of creating that he had done.*
>
> —Genesis 2:1-3

God didn't rest on the seventh day because He was tired. He rested because everything was ________________________.

God created man on the sixth day to LIVE in the seventh day.

The Seventh Day as God Designed It

- No thought of fear, survival thinking, or sickness
- No painful labor or sweat to obtain provision
- Thoughts only on family, assignment, and purpose
- Everything needed to support life and assignment prepared and available
- An existence free from care, having the ability to focus on passions and relationships with no concerns about provision

Have you ever dreamed of winning the lottery or making it big with a get-rich-quick scheme? In what other ways do you realize you have hoped or searched for an escape from the earth curse system?

Since Adam, the quest for provision is the goal by which everything else is measured. Decisions are usually made on the basis of money and not ____________________________________.

What important decisions have you made based on money?

KNOW THIS: UNTIL YOU KNOW GOD, YOU WILL NEVER KNOW HIS DESIGN FOR YOUR LIFE. HE IS THE ONE WHO CREATED YOU.

You are a very special and unique creation with skills and potential that no one else has.

What has God shown you about your unique skills and potential?

In what ways do you think you've let the culture dictate your value or warp your identity?

You'll never discover your ____________________ until you fix the money thing.

Fear holds your ______________________ hostage, and the lack of provision holds your dreams imprisoned to the impossible.

List three dreams of your own that have been held hostage by fear or lack of provision:

KNOW THIS: PROVISION IS PRO-VISION.

Without provision, there is no vision; there is only ____________.

The definition of perspective is: ________________________________

____

____

You can't just look at yourself based on where you live, what you have, and your present circumstances and judge your potential.

You have to look at your _________________________ potential.

You have to start dreaming again.

The two main reasons people don't have more income are:

1. They are trapped under the earth curse system of poverty and don't know of God's Kingdom and His principles of ____.
2. They have stinking negative ____________________.

KNOW THIS: YOU WILL NEVER POSSESS WHAT YOU CAN'T SEE. 

Having a Plan Makes All the Difference

The God that made you knows the plan. You just need to hear it.

Write out Jeremiah 29:11:

When you begin to understand and learn how the Kingdom of God operates and what the Kingdom of God says you ______________ have, your perspective will change.

______________________ is power.

List two things you learned about the Kingdom from Don's story in this chapter:

Resting Place

Take time this week to write these two perspective-changing statements somewhere where you will see them multiple times per day. Read them aloud each time you see them:

> "THERE IS MORE OUT THERE THAN I SEE RIGHT NOW."
>
> "I AM MORE THAN I SEE RIGHT NOW."

Lord, help me to conquer any slavery mind-sets or stinking thinking I may have that doesn't line up with Your Word, so I don't miss a single opportunity You are sending my way or the incredible destiny You have planned for me.

I thank You for opening my heart, my mind, and my eyes to Your perspective, for helping me dream BIG dreams, and for giving me the plans for achieving them!

In Jesus's name I pray, amen.

CHAPTER 4
I FOUND A MAJOR KEY OF THE KINGDOM!

REST [rest] – to be placed or supported so as to stay in a specified position; an instance or period of relaxing or ceasing to engage in strenuous or stressful activity; relief or freedom, especially from anything that wearies, troubles, or disturbs.

The key to something gives you access to what is protected inside or the authority to utilize the item.

The Law of Jurisdiction

The Kingdom operates on the basis of laws that you can learn and apply to your life.

Understanding a Kingdom law allows you to ________________ the results whenever you need to.

When Jesus blessed the bread and fish in Mark 6:35-44, the fish and bread changed ____________________________________.

The word *bless* means ____.

Essentially, the jurisdiction over the bread and fish changed. God now had the ___________________ right to multiply the bread and fish for the people.

KNOW THIS: TO TRULY HAVE REST IN TODAY'S WORLD, WE NEED TO BE CONFIDENT IN GOD'S PROTECTION.

When YOU __________________ about something, it brings that problem or issue under the jurisdiction of the Kingdom of God.

Write out 1 Thessalonians 5:17:

Write out James 4:2:

What does it mean to be a citizen of the Kingdom of God?

What legal rights do you now know you have as a citizen of the Kingdom of God that you didn't realize were yours?

Resting Place

This week, ask God to make you a "spiritual scientist," and take time to dive into His Word as much as possible. Be sure to record everything He reveals to you about His Kingdom and your rights as a citizen.

Lord, thank You for making me a "spiritual scientist" and revealing so many incredible things from Your Word and from this book to me that I've never seen or known before. I love learning how Your Kingdom operates and seeing my life radically changed as a result!

I praise You that Your Kingdom has laws that never change and that I am growing every day in my knowledge of those laws. Help me to not leave problems and issues under the jurisdiction of the world's system but to bring them under the jurisdiction of Your Kingdom, so I can live in victory.

In Jesus's name I pray, amen.

CHAPTER 5

FLYING IS BETTER THAN WALKING

REST [rest] – to be placed or supported so as to stay in a specified position; an instance or period of relaxing or ceasing to engage in strenuous or stressful activity; relief or freedom, especially from anything that wearies, troubles, or disturbs.

God Isn't Holding Out on You

The mind-set you want to have when you sow into the Kingdom is that God will show you the harvest and give you the __________ to capture it.

Stay within your ______________ faith and ability.

Start where you are and begin applying Kingdom law and building your ______________ in the laws of the Kingdom and your ability to capture what God shows you.

What do you think your lack of understanding has prevented you from being able to envision for your life?

How is your growing understanding of the Kingdom changing your vision for your life?

Write out Proverbs 10:22:

Laws pay no attention to who you are.

What are some ways you've let who you are or where you come from keep you from envisioning a better future for yourself?

The Blessing of the Lord is the ________________ made between God and Abraham and his heirs.

Specifically, the Blessing was the promises given to Abraham in that covenant.

A legal agreement has in it the duties and obligations of both parties involved, but it also spells out the ________________ to each.

The promises of God given to Abraham as a legal agreement ________________ the earth curse system of poverty.

KNOW THIS: THE BLESSING GIVEN TO ABRAHAM MADE IT LEGAL FOR GOD TO BLESS ABRAHAM AND HIS LINEAGE—YOU—WITH THE PROSPERITY AND INFLUENCE THAT HE WANTS MAN TO HAVE!

Read Deuteronomy 28:1-14 and list the promises:

We access these promises through our ______________________ ________________________________ under the new covenant.

The Effects of The Blessing of the Lord

- Results that allow you to focus on your assignment rather than on survival
- Finding your niche, passion point, and destiny
- Contentment
- God's wisdom, leading you to make right decisions and warning you of possible pitfalls

You have access to heaven's power to help you prosper in life.

It's not difficult to catch fish if God shows you where they are.

In what areas of your life do you need a plan from God so you can "fly" instead of "walk"?

Resting Place

In Luke 5, we saw that Peter, James, and John had fished all night and caught nothing. But when they received the plan from Jesus, everything changed.

This week, ask God what you need to do to prepare for your "catch." Do you have "nets" to clean, care for, or purchase? Ask Him what part you need to play, and take action on whatever He tells you to do.

> *Lord, thank You that You never intended for me to try to do things in my own strength. I repent for all of the times that I've tried!*
>
> *I praise You that I am not bound to the earth curse system and that ALL of Your blessings are evident in my life! Thank You that I am blessed everywhere I go and in everything I put my hands to!*
>
> *In Jesus's name I pray, amen.*

CHAPTER 6

THERE IS MORE TO LIFE THAN PAYING THE BILLS!

REST [rest] – to be placed or supported so as to stay in a specified position; an instance or period of relaxing or ceasing to engage in strenuous or stressful activity; relief or freedom, especially from anything that wearies, troubles, or disturbs.

In what ways have you been living under financial stress, focused only on surviving?

The Sabbath Rest

Write out Matthew 6:25:

Everything in life is here to support your life and your____.

> If you had no need for money—had more money than you could ever spend in your lifetime—what would you do?

Man was created at the end of the sixth day to dwell with God on the seventh day, the day of _______________.

When Adam fell, God gave him a remembrance—a picture—of what He would someday restore back to His creation. It was called ____.

The word *Sabbath* literally means ______________________________________.

The Sabbath Requirements:

- No work. No sweating. No painful toil.
- Man was to stop, enjoy his family, and worship God.
- All provisions for the Sabbath were to be completed prior to the beginning of the Sabbath.
- A day of rest with full provision and every detail of possible need already attended to.
- Man could stop and think of something other than survival.

Mankind's quest for wealth is a symptom of the desire to be ________________ from the painful toil and sweat that has held us prisoner our entire lives.

Wealth lures us with the possible escape to a place of ____________ —a place where we can focus on what we really want to do, where we can live lives full of _____________________ instead of survival.

KNOW THIS: HOW WE ACKNOWLEDGE AND CELEBRATE THE SABBATH MAY HAVE CHANGED, BUT THE TRUE PICTURE OF THE SABBATH HAS NOT CHANGED.

Write out Hebrews 4:9-11:

There is a Sabbath rest available for the people of God ___________.

God's rest says everything is whole, complete, and provision is readily available. You can have freedom from the survival mentality, freedom from being imprisoned by poverty, and freedom from sickness and disease. There are new options!

Read and then re-read this excerpt from *Your Financial Revolution: The Power of Rest*, and write your thoughts:

> *The Sabbath did the same thing. Its shadow said to not work, no painful toil and sweat. It was only a shadow, however, not the real thing. But it was pointing to Jesus Christ, who has, in fact, set us free from the curse of the law and the earth curse system and reestablished us as sons and daughters of God and citizens of God's great Kingdom! Again, it was a picture of what Jesus would bring back to us someday. It is a finished work where everything we need for life has been restored back to us. However, as Hebrews says, we enter into this rest through faith. Remember, faith is required to make it legal for heaven to have jurisdiction here in the earth realm. On the cross Jesus cried out, "It is finished!" just as God said it was finished at the end of the sixth day.*

The Sabbath is not a religious day.

_________________________ is the true Sabbath, and in Him we find access to the Kingdom of God and all that it has. Thus, we can rest!

God uses the number ___________________ to show that everything is complete.

> How has this chapter affected or changed how you may have previously thought of the Sabbath?

Resting Place

Take some time this week to really think about whether the things you have in your life are supporting your purpose or if some thing, or things, have become more important than your life's purpose.

Follow that up by looking back at your response to the question at the beginning of this chapter: *If you had no need for money, had more money than you could ever spend in your lifetime, what would you do?*

Ask God to reveal to you what you might need to change to take the next step toward the destiny He has planned for you.

> *Lord, I ask for forgiveness for any times I've run after wealth, given in to the pressure to perform, or worried about my future instead of trusting in Your plan for my life. Help me to have a clearer understanding than ever before of what the Sabbath rest truly is and how I can live in it!*
>
> *In Jesus's name I pray, amen.*

CHAPTER 7

THIS IS IMPOSSIBLE!

REST [rest] – to be placed or supported so as to stay in a specified position; an instance or period of relaxing or ceasing to engage in strenuous or stressful activity; relief or freedom, especially from anything that wearies, troubles, or disturbs.

Are You Celebrating?

The Year of Jubilee is the greatest picture of what Jesus wants to do in your finances.

In this chapter, I share how God dealt with me about my small thinking and let me know that I should be enjoying the Jubilee. But I wasn't. I had some changes to make.

What about you? Are you enjoying the Jubilee?

Wait. Don't write your answer to that question. Instead, answer these:

When was the last time you created something?

What dysfunction have you been putting up with in your life?

The Year of Jubilee, in essence, meant that Israel did not have a harvest for ________ years in a row. Then, they had to wait during the third year for those crops to mature and be harvested before they could replenish their food supply. Naturally, they didn't see how that was possible.

Write out what God said to them from Leviticus 25:20-22:

How does what God told the Israelites parallel creation? (Hint: Look back at chapter 3.)

God was showing Israel a picture of ________________________ __________________, which stands in stark contrast to the earth curse system of painful toil and sweat.

God wanted them to see Him as their ______________________ and to understand that He provides with a mighty provision.

The Year of Jubilee also shows us:

1. The __________ also rested.
2. All land was to be returned to its _________________ owner. This gave them back their ability to have prosperity.
3. All ___________ were to be set free and returned to their families.

KNOW THIS: LIKE THE ISRAELITES, YOUR PROSPERITY AND FREEDOM HAVE BEEN RETURNED TO YOU. THE INHERITANCE AND PROSPERITY OF GOD'S KINGDOM IS YOURS AGAIN.

Jesus:

√ Gave us back what Adam lost.

√ Set us free from slavery, making us sons and daughters of God.

√ Freed us from the earth curse system of painful toil and sweat, allowing God to bless the work of our hands in a mighty way.

Jesus paid for all these things, but you MUST know how to appropriate these benefits into your life here in the earth realm.

You have to understand that the Kingdom operates by laws, and you have to know your legal rights as a son or daughter and a citizen!

God does NOT arbitrarily choose who He wants to bless!

What sticks out to you the most about the three stories at the end of this chapter?

Resting Place

God told the Israelites He would provide more than enough.

More than enough.

Freedom from the rat race. From slavery to having options. Free to find and prosper in your purpose and passion. No worries. Every need taken care of.

That's what God intended for you.

Purpose to take some time this week to rest physically, and reread chapter 7 in *Your Financial Revolution: The Power of Rest* with confidence that God has already provided you with more than enough.

Lord, I ask You to show me any areas of my life in which I've been putting up with dysfunction or have accepted it as normal. Reveal to me any areas of my life in which I'm guilty of thinking too small or where I've gotten stale. Help me to see You as my provider and to understand that You provide with MIGHTY provision.

I pray that You teach me to be the dreamer and creator You've made me to be, so I can do my part and see HUGE, Year-of-Jubilee-sized blessings in my own life.

In Jesus's name I pray, amen.

CHAPTER 8

THE DOUBLE PORTION

REST [rest] – to be placed or supported so as to stay in a specified position; an instance or period of relaxing or ceasing to engage in strenuous or stressful activity; relief or freedom, especially from anything that wearies, troubles, or disturbs.

The Year of Jubilee and the Sabbath year preceding it were both only possible because of the _______________ harvest that occurred in the sixth year—the double portion.

Steadfast Reliance

God used the process with the manna to ____________________ the nation to look to Him each day for their food, of course, but also for everything in their lives.

THE SABBATH REST IS _______________________ WITHOUT THE DOUBLE PORTION!

Unless you have more than enough, you will never have ______________________________ from the running and sweating of the earth curse system.

KNOW THIS: IT DOESN'T MATTER WHAT YOUR LIFE LOOKS LIKE RIGHT NOW. LOOK TO WHAT GOD SAYS, AND START EXPECTING WHAT THE KINGDOM SAYS ABOUT YOU. FAITH IS STAYING IN AGREEMENT WITH WHAT GOD SAYS, NOT YOUR CIRCUMSTANCES.

The story of the Prodigal Son in Luke 15:11-32 teaches us several important keys about the double portion.

1. The younger son has ____________________ received his share of his inheritance; he can make no further claim on the estate.

2. The younger son left his father's house, implying he left behind his provision, his protection, and the __________ of the nation in which his father's house resides.

3. For the first time in his entire existence, the younger son begs to be paid as a ________________, a hireling, doing manual labor—a perversion of his true identity as a son.

4. The younger son becomes so desperate that he loses sight of any ________________________ his life may have had.

5. The father willingly became unclean on behalf of his son, and the younger son, although undeserving, is given back the position and ____________________ of being a son, openly and freely honored as a son, and completely restored to his former position as a son in the house.

6. Although the younger brother had already received his share of the estate, he was reinstated as a son and now was enjoying a second portion.

KNOW THIS: YOU HAVE THE DOUBLE PORTION. YOU ARE A SON OR DAUGHTER OF GOD AND SHOULD BE ENJOYING AN INHERITANCE YOU FREELY RECEIVE FROM YOUR FATHER.

Resting Place

In Exodus 16:21-30, we see how God used manna to teach the Israelites to rely on Him for their provision. Take some time this week to ask God to reveal to you any areas of your life in which you have not been relying on Him.

Write down what He reveals to you and pray, releasing those areas to Him.

Lord, I ask for forgiveness for any times I have relied on myself and not steadfastly relied on You. I give these areas of my life [name them here] to you fully, with confidence that You are my source and supply.

I praise You that I have been redeemed and restored to You through Jesus! And I thank You that You ALWAYS and freely provide more than enough—Your double portion—as my loving Father, not based on what I do but on who I am in Christ!

In Jesus's name I pray, amen.

CHAPTER 9

MORE THAN ENOUGH!

REST [rest] – to be placed or supported so as to stay in a specified position; an instance or period of relaxing or ceasing to engage in strenuous or stressful activity; relief or freedom, especially from anything that wearies, troubles, or disturbs.

As a child of God it is your legal right to enjoy the goodness and the prosperity of your Father's house.

Starting Your Journey to Freedom

Your journey to freedom begins in your _______________. Unless your thoughts agree with the Word of God, you will never enjoy His benefits.

KNOW THIS: GOD'S WORD CANNOT FAIL, AND IT WILL BRING A CHANGE TO ANY CIRCUMSTANCE.

Write out Hebrews 4:9-10:

The Sabbath rest is a ________________ to every New Testament believer in Christ.

As believers, we are called to live out of the financial ______________________________ of our lives.

THIS IS IMPORTANT!

Just because God shows you something doesn't mean it's time to move on it.

Many times, He shows you something to give you ______________ and time for __________________.

____________________ is just as important as hearing direction in the first place

Have you ever jumped out too soon and missed God's timing? Give an example.

Read this confession version of Isaiah 61:7-9 out loud:

> *Instead of shame, I will receive a double portion. Instead of disgrace, I will rejoice in my inheritance. I will inherit a double portion in my land, and everlasting joy will be mine. For the Lord loves justice and hates robbery and iniquity. In His faithfulness, He will reward me and make an everlasting covenant with me. My descendants will be known among the nations and my offspring among the peoples. All who see me will acknowledge that I am a person the Lord has blessed.*

Write out Mark 11:24:

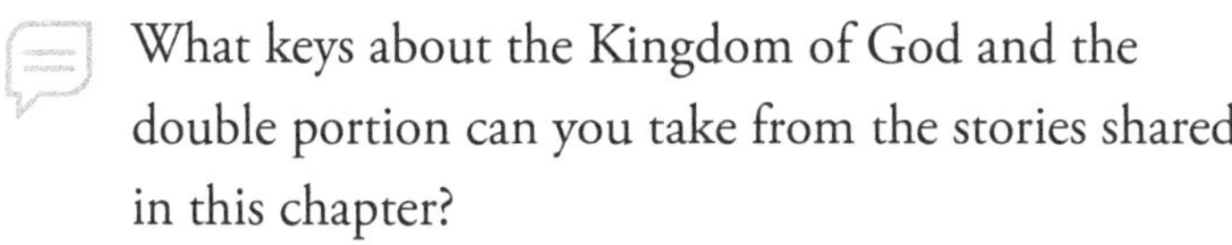

What keys about the Kingdom of God and the double portion can you take from the stories shared in this chapter?

The double portion is not limited to having or receiving _______________ of something.

The double portion is simply having more than enough, or having something abundantly supplied.

KNOW THIS: HOLD *THINGS* LOOSELY, AND PURSUE THE KING AND HIS KINGDOM, AND YOU WILL FIND MORE THAN ENOUGH—THE DOUBLE PORTION!

Resting Place

Your journey to freedom begins with your thoughts. You can choose what you think about. You don't have to think on everything that pops into your head.

The Bible says that we're to take every thought captive and make it obedient to Christ. Plain and simple, your brain does not have the authority to think anything it wants.

This week, test *every* thought you have against God's will for you. How do you know His will? It's made known to us in His Word, the Bible. Measure everything against what God says. Umpire your thoughts. If they don't line up with what God says, get them out by replacing them with a right thought.

Lord, I thank You that Your Word says that You are able to do immeasurably more than all I can ask or imagine according to Your power that is at work within me! I stand on this Scripture, knowing that Your power is at work in me, renewing my mind to Your Truth, replacing all wrong thoughts with right ones, and moving me forward into the destiny You've designed for me.

In Jesus's name I pray, amen.

”

CHAPTER 10

THE MYSTERY OF THE DOUBLE PORTION

REST [rest] – to be placed or supported so as to stay in a specified position; an instance or period of relaxing or ceasing to engage in strenuous or stressful activity; relief or freedom, especially from anything that wearies, troubles, or disturbs.

Now that you know what the Sabbath rest is and how it is possible through the double portion, you need to know how to tap into the double portion.

Time to Take Action

There is more to the Kingdom than just being _________________.

Many Christians are in a state of being satisfied but miss the double portion that brings the Sabbath rest of God.

KNOW THIS: SATISFIED EATS FOR TODAY; THE DOUBLE PORTION BUILDS A TOMORROW!

The only thing that can actually change your life is the _________________ _____________________.

You must see past being satisfied to _________ the double portion.

In John 6:11-12, we see that Jesus told the disciples to go and _________________ the pieces, or ___________________, and let ___________________ be wasted.

There is no Sabbath rest without gathering ____________________ than you need.

Jesus was teaching His disciples to look past being satisfied and to see the full ____________________ of the Kingdom.

God **had already given them the Sabbath rest**, the double portion. They just didn't see it!

KNOW THIS: GOD IS NEVER GOING TO JUST SUPPLY SATISFIED; HE WILL ALWAYS SUPPLY MORE THAN ENOUGH. YOU JUST MAY NOT BE SEEING IT!

Write out Luke 6:38:

The "running over" is the double portion!

You must __________________________ the overflow!

Most of the time, your provision will not be in the form of raw dollar bills. It will be in the form of _________________, divine appointments, and ______________________ by the Holy Spirit.

You must be prepared with a proper understanding of the double portion, so you don't walk right by it because of your earth curse survival training!

How do you need to start seizing the moments in your life?

God ______________________ provides at the double portion level.

The problem is that we don't even know to ________________ for it!

Satan's intent is to keep you broke all the days of your life and enslaved to a meager survival lifestyle where you have no influence.

______________________ is influence!

Why is the double portion hidden?

What fragments do you realize you haven't been gathering in your life?

The double portion is captured through ________________. This is simply something that the Holy Spirit is showing you that you wouldn't have known on your own.

In what areas of your life do you need revelation knowledge this week?

In what areas of your life do you realize you have been limiting God?

Resting Place

Habakkuk 2:2 tells us to write the vision and make it plain.

This week, take some time to think and pray about your future, and create a vision board that will help you take action toward your destiny.

Lord, I thank You that You have already given me everything I need to LIVE in the Sabbath rest. Open my eyes and reveal to me exactly where I need to gather the fragments I've been missing! Help me to never miss an idea, a divine appointment, or a single direction the Holy Spirit is giving me, so I can fully capture my double portion!

In Jesus's name I pray, amen.

ANSWER KEY

Chapter One

The world's "Hamster Wheel" system will have you constantly running and running and running but still ending up in the exact same place you started.

The Kingdom of God is a government, with laws that do not change.

One idea from God can completely change your life.

When you are living in God's rest, you can stay on assignment and keep focused on your purpose.

When you're no longer living a life of survival, you can be about life.

Chapter Two

In the literal sense, kingdom means the king's dominion.

A king's kingdom operates by the word of the king.

His words become the laws that govern his domain and the lives of his citizens.

Ephesians 2:19 says you are not only a citizen of the Kingdom of God but also a member of His very own household, a son or daughter of the King.

You don't have to feel like a citizen of a country in order to be one.

It is a legal matter that is satisfied by the fact that you were born there.

If you ask according to the laws of the King, you should already know that He will enforce His own law. Thus, you can be confident in the outcome; there will be no guessing.

God's Kingdom is governed by laws, which are available to every citizen without partiality.

Read Mark 6:4-6 again. These Scriptures give us insight into how the Kingdom functions. Here, we see Jesus could not do any miracles in His hometown. Why? Because of their lack of faith.

What does fail, however, is God's jurisdiction, His ability to intervene in the earth realm, which is produced by our faith.

Faith is agreement with heaven.

After Adam, who had the authority over the earth, cut off God's legal jurisdiction in the earth realm, God told him that his survival would be up to him, with hard labor and painful toil. I call this the earth curse system of survival.

God has to find a man or a woman in the earth realm who will come into agreement with Him, which opens the spiritual door for the Kingdom of God to have legal jurisdiction here.

Faith must be present for the Kingdom of God to have jurisdiction here.

Chapter Three

God didn't rest on the seventh day because He was tired. He rested because everything was complete.

Since Adam, the quest for provision is the goal by which everything else is measured. Decisions are usually made on the basis of money and not purpose.

You'll never discover your destiny until you fix the money thing.

Fear holds your dreams hostage, and the lack of provision holds your dreams imprisoned to the impossible.

Without provision there is no vision; there is only survival.

The definition of perspective is: a particular attitude toward or a way of regarding something; a point of view, attitude, frame of reference, or interpretation. Basically, perspective is really just how you think about something.

You have to look at your created potential.

The two main reasons people don't have more income are:

1. They are trapped under the earth curse system of poverty and don't know of God's Kingdom and His principles of provision.

2. They have stinking negative thinking.

When you begin to understand and learn how the Kingdom of God operates and what the Kingdom of God says you already have, your perspective will change.

Knowledge is power.

Chapter Four

Understanding a Kingdom law allows you to duplicate the results whenever you need to.

When Jesus blessed the bread and fish in Mark 6:35-44, the fish and bread changed kingdoms.

The word bless means to sanctify or to separate.

Essentially, the jurisdiction over the bread and fish changed. God then had the legal right to multiply the bread and fish for the people.

When YOU pray about something, it brings that problem or issue under the jurisdiction of the Kingdom of God.

Chapter Five

The mind-set you want to have when you sow into the Kingdom is that God will show you the harvest and give you the plan to capture it.

Stay within your developed faith and ability.

Start where you are and begin applying Kingdom law and building your confidence in the laws of the Kingdom and your ability to capture what God shows you.

The Blessing of the Lord is the covenant made between God and Abraham and his heirs.

A legal agreement has in it the duties and obligations of both parties involved, but it also spells out the benefits to each.

The promises of God given to Abraham as a legal agreement overrode the earth curse system of poverty.

We access these promises through our faith in Jesus Christ under the new covenant.

Chapter Six

Everything in life is here to support your life and your purpose.

Man was created at the end of the sixth day to dwell with God on the seventh day, the day of rest.

When Adam fell, God gave him a remembrance—a picture—of what He would someday restore back to His creation. It was called the Sabbath.

The word Sabbath literally means rest.

Mankind's quest for wealth is a symptom of the desire to be free from the painful toil and sweat that has held us prisoner our entire lives.

Wealth lures us with the possible escape to a place of rest—a place where we can focus on what we really want to do, where we can live lives full of purpose instead of survival.

There is a Sabbath rest available for the people of God today.

Jesus is the true Sabbath, and in Him we find access to the Kingdom of God and all that it has. Thus, we can rest!

God uses the number seven to show that everything is complete.

Chapter Seven

The Year of Jubilee, in essence, meant that Israel did not have a harvest for three years in a row. Then, they had to wait during the third year for those crops to mature and be harvested before they could replenish their food supply. Naturally, they didn't see how that was possible.

God was showing Israel a picture of more than enough, which stands in stark contrast to the earth curse system of painful toil and sweat.

God wanted them to see Him as their provider and to understand that He provides with a mighty provision.

The Year of Jubilee also shows us:

1. The land also rested.
2. All land was to be returned to its original owner. This gave them back their ability to have prosperity.
3. All slaves were to be set free and returned to their families.

Chapter Eight

The Year of Jubilee and the Sabbath year preceding it were both only possible because of the huge harvest that occurred in the sixth year—the double portion.

God used the process with the manna to train the nation to look to Him each day for their food, of course, but also for everything in their lives.

THE SABBATH REST IS <u>IMPOSSIBLE</u> WITHOUT THE DOUBLE PORTION!

Unless you have more than enough, you will never have <u>rest</u> from the running and sweating of the earth curse system.

The story of The Prodigal Son in Luke 15:11-32 teaches us several important keys about the double portion.

1. The younger son has <u>already</u> received his share of his inheritance; he can make no further claim on the estate.

2. The younger son left his father's house, implying he left behind his provision, his protection, and the <u>laws</u> of the nation in which his father's house resides.

3. For the first time in his entire existence, the younger son begs to be paid as a <u>servant</u>, a hireling, doing manual labor—a perversion of his true identity as a son.

4. The younger son becomes so desperate that he loses sight of any <u>purpose</u> his life may have had.

5. The father willingly became unclean on behalf of his son, and the younger son, although undeserving, is given back the position and <u>benefits</u> of being a son, openly and freely honored as a son, and completely restored to his former position as a son in the house.

Chapter Nine

Your journey to freedom begins in your thinking. Unless your thoughts agree with the Word of God, you will never enjoy His benefits.

The Sabbath rest is a promise to every New Testament believer in Christ.

As believers, we are called to live out of the financial overflow of our lives.

THIS IS IMPORTANT!

> Just because God shows you something doesn't mean it's time to move on it.
>
> Many times, He shows you something to give you direction and time for preparation.
>
> Timing is just as important as hearing direction in the first place.

The double portion is not limited to having or receiving two of something.

Chapter Ten

There is more to the Kingdom than just being satisfied.

The only thing that can actually change your life is the double portion.

You must see past being satisfied to capture the double portion.

In John 6:11-12, we see that Jesus told the disciples to go and gather the pieces, or fragments, and let nothing be wasted.

There is no Sabbath rest without gathering more than you need.

Jesus was teaching His disciples to look past being satisfied and to see the full provision of the Kingdom.

You must capture the overflow!

Most of the time, your provision will not be in the form of raw dollar bills. It will be in the form of ideas, divine appointments, and direction by the Holy Spirit.

God always provides at the double portion level.

The problem is that we don't even know to look for it!

Money is influence!

Why is the double portion hidden? Because Satan hates when we step into the overflow and the Sabbath rest, so he tries to intercept and steal the double portion. This is why God does not openly reveal His treasures.

The double portion is captured through revelation. This is simply something that the Holy Spirit is showing you that you wouldn't have known on your own.